GRAPHIC SCIENCE

A JOURNEY INTO

ADAPTATION

WITH

SUPER SCIENTIST

Agnieszka Biskup

illustrated by Cynthia Martin
and Barbara Schulz

www.raintreepublishers.co.uk
Visit our website to find out
more information about
Raintree books.

To order:
☎ Phone +44 (0) 1865 888066
▤ Fax +44 (0) 1865 314091
▣ Visit www.raintreepublishers.co.uk

Raintree is an imprint of Capstone Global Library Limited, a company incorporated in England and Wales having its registered office at 7 Pilgrim Street, London EC4V 6LB
Registered company number: 6695882

"Raintree" is a registered trademark of Pearson Education Limited, under licence to Capstone Global Library Limited

Text © Capstone Press 2008
First published by Capstone Press in 2008
First published in hardback in the United Kingdom by Capstone Global Library in 2010
The moral rights of the proprietor have been asserted.

ISBN 978 1 4062 1465 9 (hardback)
14 13 12 11 10

British Library Cataloguing in Publication Data
Biskup, Agnieszka.
Adaptation. -- (Graphic science)
578.4-dc22
A full catalogue record for this book is available from the British Library.

Art Director and Designer: Bob Lentz
Cover Artist: Tod Smith
Colourist: Krista Ward
UK Editor: Diyan Leake
UK Production: Alison Parsons
Originated by Capstone Global Library
Printed and bound in China by South China Printing Company Limited

Acknowledgements
The publisher would like to thank the following for permission to reproduce copyright material:
Charles Darwin Research Station p. 8; Corbis pp. 7 (Joe McDonald), 14 (Kevin Schafer),
25 (Dan Guravich).

Disclaimer
All the Internet addresses (URLs) given in this book were valid at the time of going to press.
However, due to the dynamic nature of the Internet, some addresses may have changed, or sites may
have changed or ceased to exist since publication. While the publisher regrets any inconvenience this
may cause readers, no responsibility for any such changes can be accepted by the publisher.

Contents

Using bushes for cover, Super Scientist Max Axiom begins his adventures in adaptation from his own back garden.

I'm always amazed by the wonders of nature.

My back garden serves as a habitat for the animals that live here.

It provides the food, water, and shelter they need to survive.

4

But wings are not this hawk's only adaptation. Its feathers also help it fly and stay warm.

Its excellent eyesight, sharp claws, and curved beak help the hawk catch and kill the small animals it eats.

Together, all of these adaptations help the hawk survive in its habitat.

FLYING SQUIRREL

ACCESS GRANTED: MAX AXIOM

Is it a bird? Is it a plane? No – it's a squirrel! The flying squirrel has a fold of skin connecting the wrists of its front legs to the ankles of its back legs. This fold of skin helps the squirrel glide from tree branch to tree branch. With a good jump, flying squirrels can glide over 9 metres through the air.

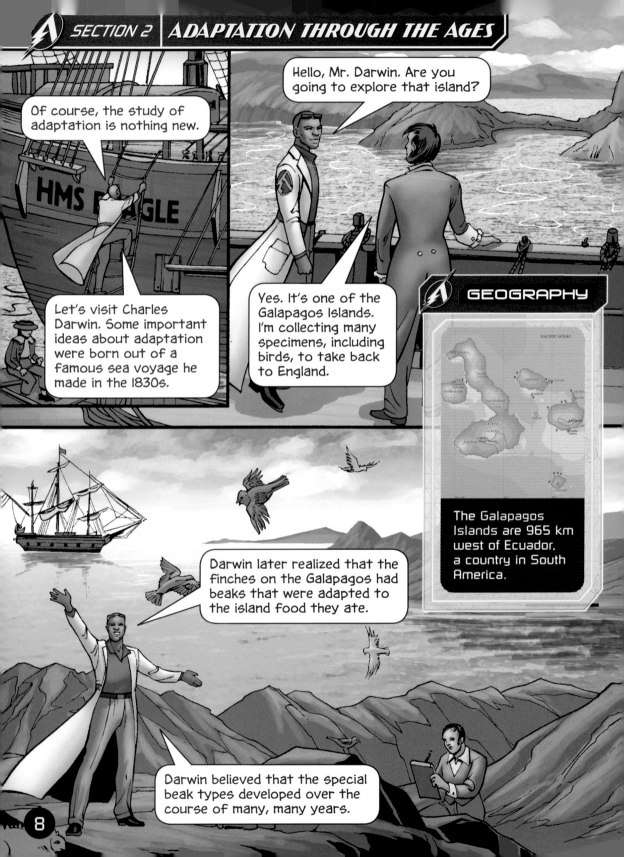

Actually, most animals need many generations to adapt to their environments. Rapid changes in an environment make survival very difficult.

The dinosaurs found this out the hard way 65 million years ago.

The meteorite's impact threw huge amounts of dust and ash into the air. This debris blocked out the sun's light and temperatures fell.

KA-BOOM!

Why did the dinosaurs go extinct? No one knows for sure. But some scientists believe that the climate changed quickly after a meteorite the size of a mountain hit earth.

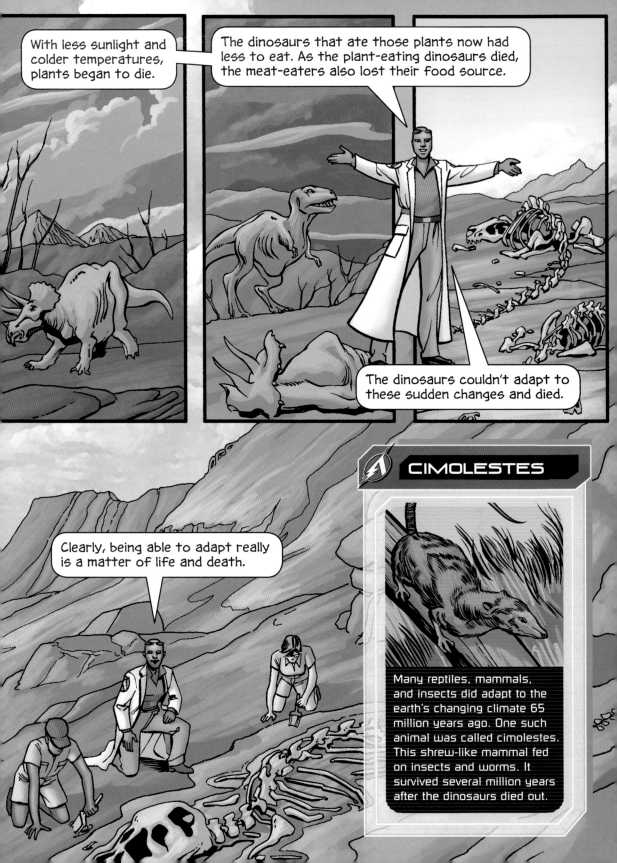

Although many animals die because they can't adapt, some do adapt and survive. Take a look at Britain's peppered moths.

In the early 1800s, peppered moths came in two varieties, light and dark.

Before 1850, dark peppered moths were rare.

Their dark bodies on pale tree branches made them easy targets for birds and other predators.

The body features, or physical adaptations, of plants and animals often relate to the environments they live in.

For example, a camel's hump is an adaptation for desert life. When food and water are scarce, the camel uses fat stored in its hump for energy.

The camel's long eyelashes and fuzzy ear hair protect its eyes and ears from blowing sand.

CREOSOTE BUSH

Plants also cope with dry desert conditions. Since plants lose water through their leaves, the creosote bush has adapted. Its leaves have a waxy coating to help the plant hold in water.

BARREL CACTUS

In many cases, plants lack leaves altogether. The barrel cactus stores water in its fleshy stem.

 FENNEC FOX

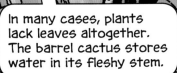

ACCESS GRANTED: MAX AXIOM

Is fur a good adaptation for the desert? For the fennec fox it is. This fox's fur keeps it warm at night when the desert is cold. During the day, the light-coloured fur reflects sunlight to help keep the fox cool.

Hi, Dr. Diaz. What are you studying today?

But what about places like rainforests that are hot and very wet? How do living things adapt to these conditions?

I know a biologist just ahead who studies rainforest plant life. I bet he sees adaptations every day.

Hello, Max. I'm glad you found me. I'm taking samples of this philodendron plant.

Wow, this leaf feels waxy. Back in the desert, some plants had waxy leaves to hold in water.

That's true, but the waxy coating has a different purpose in the rainforest. It helps plants repel extra water like a raincoat.

In fact, many rainforest plants also have drip tips to help them shed water. These features prevent the growth of bacteria and fungi on the plants.

DRIP TIP

15

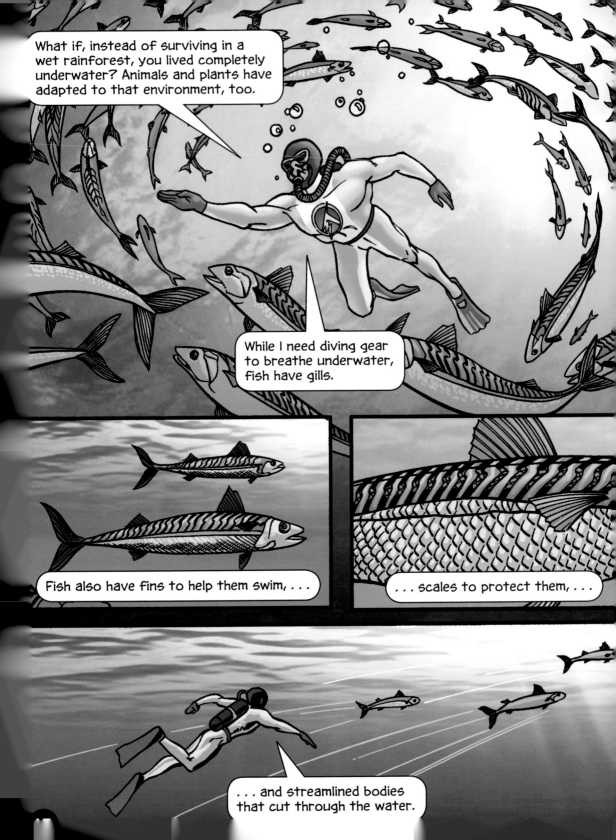

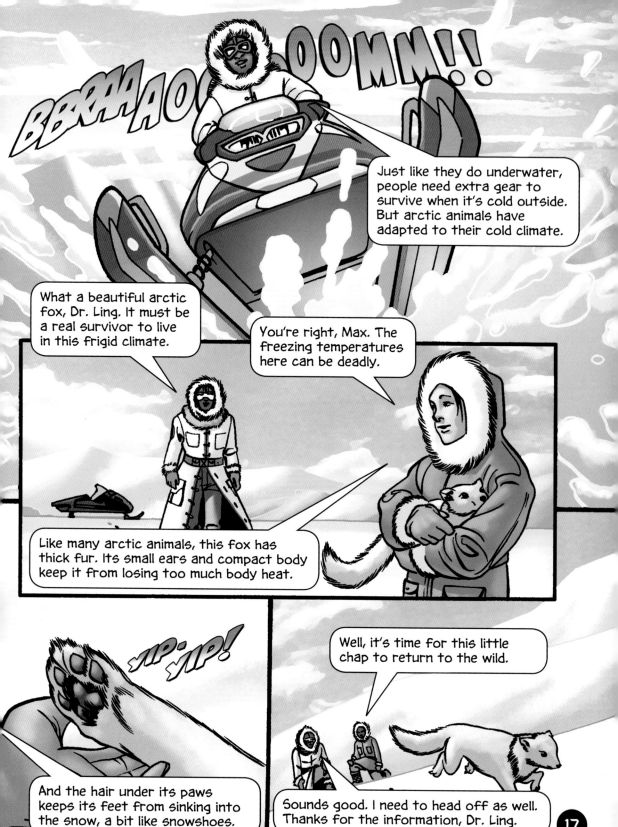

BBRRAAOOOOMM!!

Just like they do underwater, people need extra gear to survive when it's cold outside. But arctic animals have adapted to their cold climate.

What a beautiful arctic fox, Dr. Ling. It must be a real survivor to live in this frigid climate.

You're right, Max. The freezing temperatures here can be deadly.

Like many arctic animals, this fox has thick fur. Its small ears and compact body keep it from losing too much body heat.

YIP! YIP!

Well, it's time for this little chap to return to the wild.

And the hair under its paws keeps its feet from sinking into the snow, a bit like snowshoes.

Sounds good. I need to head off as well. Thanks for the information, Dr. Ling.

17

Adaptations are not only about physical features. The way animals behave helps them survive too.

For instance, a porcupine thrusts out its quills when it feels threatened.

YELP!

The hognose snake becomes a great actor when threatened. First it pretends to twist with pain. Then it turns upside down, throws back its head, opens its mouth, and sticks out its tongue.

Why does it behave like this? It plays dead because most predators prefer to catch their prey alive.

Along with predators, animals also face harsh conditions in their habitats.

Mice, squirrels, skunks, and bears live in areas where food is scarce during long winters. To survive they hibernate.

During hibernation, animals go into what appears to be a deep sleep.

MAX AXIOM

Animals that hibernate slow down their body functions. Their heart and breathing rates slow. They don't eat for weeks or months. They live on fat stored in the body.

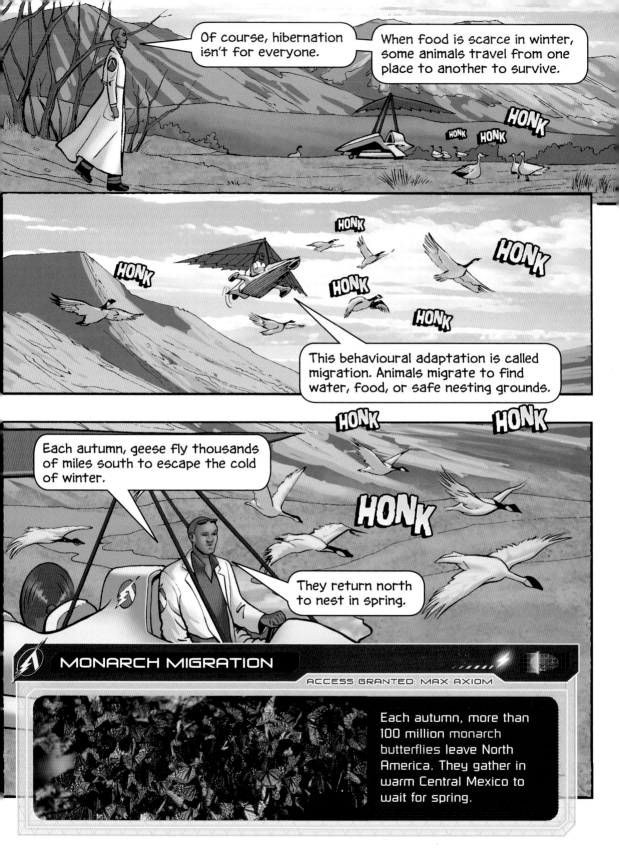

A rose bush's thorns protect its stems from being eaten.

A woodpecker's beak helps it to bore into trees to find insects.

A rabbit freezes in its tracks when it feels threatened, helping it blend in with its surroundings.

Everywhere you look, you will find ways that plants and animals have adapted to survive in their habitats.

Take a look around.

You may be surprised by what you discover.

Not all flowers smell sweet. In fact, the flowers of the rafflesia plant have adapted to smell just like rotten meat. They give off this horrible smell to attract flies. The flies then carry the rafflesia's pollen to other flowers.

 The mimic octopus is a master of mimicry. By changing its shape and colour, it can look like sole fish, sea snakes, or lionfish. Scientists believe the octopus developed its mimicry skills because its normal habitat doesn't allow it many places to hide from predators.

 Some tube worms, crabs, and clams live at the bottom of the sea without sunlight or plant life. These animals have adapted to feed on bacteria that grow on the sulfur-rich chemicals spewing from active underwater volcanoes.

 Keeping clean is an important behavioural adaptation. Many animals increase their chances for survival by grooming themselves and each other. Monkeys comb through each other's fur, picking off dirt and mites that might spread disease. Birds preen their feathers to remove mites and to keep their feathers in first-rate shape for flight.

 The Venus flytrap is famous for its ability to trap and digest insects that land on its leaves. This carnivorous plant has adapted to eat insects because the poor soil it lives in doesn't provide enough nutrients.

Bald rockcod have adapted to the freezing temperatures in the Antarctic Ocean. These fish have chemicals in their bodies that work just like an antifreeze liquid does in a car. The chemicals stop the fish from freezing solid in the frigid water below the Antarctic ice shelves.

 The North American wood frog has adapted to arctic winters by using an extreme form of hibernation. In winter, the frog goes into a deep sleep. Its heartbeat and breathing slow to a stop. Amazingly, much of its body freezes solid. In spring, the wood frog's body thaws and its breathing and heartbeat restart.

MORE ABOUT

SUPER SCIENTIST

Real name: Maxwell Axiom
Height: 1.86 m (6 ft 1 in.)
Weight: 87 kg (13 st. 10 lb.)
Eyes: Brown   **Hair:** None

Super capabilities: Super intelligence; able to shrink to the size of an atom; sunglasses give X-ray vision; lab coat allows for travel through time and space.

Origin: Since birth, Max Axiom seemed destined for greatness. His mother, a marine biologist, taught her son about the mysteries of the sea. His father, a nuclear physicist and volunteer park warden, showed Max the wonders of the earth and sky.

One day, while Max was hiking in the hills, a megacharged lightning bolt struck him with blinding fury. When he awoke, he discovered a new-found energy and set out to learn as much about science as possible. He travelled the globe studying every aspect of the subject. Then he was ready to share his knowledge and new identity with the world. He had become Max Axiom, Super Scientist.

GLOSSARY

bacteria very small living things. Some bacteria cause disease.

camouflage colouring or covering that makes animals, people, and objects look like their surroundings

carnivorous meat-eating. The Venus flytrap is one type of carnivorous plant.

climate the usual weather in a place

extinct no longer alive anywhere in the world

generation average amount of time between the birth of parents and that of their offspring

habitat the place and natural conditions where an animal lives

hibernate spend winter in a deep sleep

migration regular movement of animals as they search different places for food

mimic to copy the look, actions, or behaviours of another plant or animal

predator animal that hunts and eats other animals

prey animal hunted by another animal for food

reproduce breed and have offspring

specimen sample that a scientist studies closely

FIND OUT MORE

Books

Adaptation (Life Processes series), Steve Parker (Heinemann Library, 2006).

Life on Earth (Making Sense of Science series), Peter Riley (Franklin Watts, 2004)

Living Things series, Robert Snedden (Franklin Watts, 2007)

Websites

www.wwf.org.uk

Visit the World Wild Fund for Nature's website to find out what steps are being taken to protect endangered species and their habitats.

www.envirolink.org

The website provides up-to-date news and information on the environment.

 INDEX